*Mass*
*of the* BREAD
OF LIFE

Kevin
Mayhew

Margaret
Rizza

We hope you enjoy the music in this book. Further copies are available
from your local music shop or Christian bookshop.

In case of difficulty, please contact the publisher direct by writing to:

The Sales Department
KEVIN MAYHEW LTD
Rattlesden
Bury St Edmunds
Suffolk
IP30 0SZ

Phone 01449 737978
Fax 01449 737834
E-mail info@kevinmayhew.com

Please ask for our complete catalogue of outstanding Church Music.

First published in Great Britain in 1998 by Kevin Mayhew Ltd.

© Copyright 1998 Kevin Mayhew Ltd.

ISBN 1 84003 235 9
ISMN M 57004 420 7
Catalogue No: 1450110

0 1 2 3 4 5 6 7 8 9

Cover photographs: Derek Forss and Andrew Cowin.
Photo composite and cover design: Jaquetta Sergeant.

Music Editor: Donald Thomson
Music setting by Geoffrey Moore

Printed and bound in Great Britain by
Caligraving Limited Thetford Norfolk

# About the Composer

MARGARET RIZZA studied at the Royal College of Music, London, and the National School of Opera, London, and completed her operatic training in Siena and Rome. She has sung at many of the world's leading operatic venues, including La Scala, Milan, Glyndebourne, Sadler's Wells, and with the English Opera Group, and under such conductors as Benjamin Britten, Igor Stravinsky and Leonard Bernstein. She was also a frequent broadcaster.

Since 1977 she has taught singing and voice production at the Guildhall School of Music and Drama in London, and gives master-classes and workshops at summer schools. She also devotes much of her time to helping students to perform and share their music with the marginalised and with people with mental and physical disabilities. In recent years she has worked closely with music therapists.

She has trained and conducted several choirs, and is the founder of The Cameo Opera, The Cameo Singers and the St Thomas Music Group.

Since 1983 she has dedicated herself to the work of spirituality and to the wider aspect of music in the community. She has led many retreats, and is closely involved with the World Community for Christian Meditation (WCCM), as well as leading courses for prayer guides.

Also by Margaret Rizza:
*Fountain of Life: music for contemplative worship*

| | |
|---|---|
| Full score with instrumental parts | 1400147 |
| Vocal score | 1450090 |
| Melody edition | 1400148 |
| Cassette | 1480040 |
| CD | 1490024 |

# MASS OF THE BREAD OF LIFE

Margaret Rizza

## KYRIE

# GLORIA

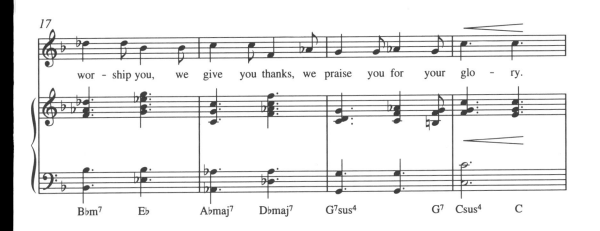

wor - ship you, we give you thanks, we praise you for your glo - ry.

B♭m⁷    E♭    A♭maj⁷    D♭maj⁷    G⁷sus⁴    G⁷   Csus⁴    C

**Optional descant**

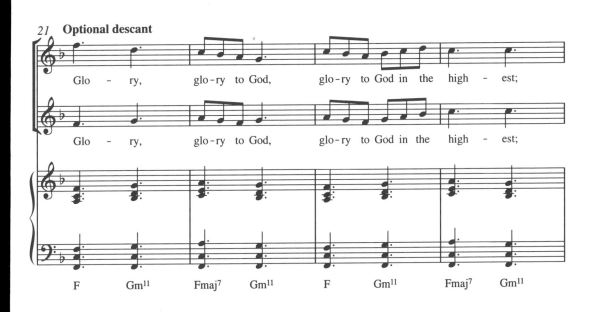

Glo - ry, glo-ry to God, glo-ry to God in the high - est;

Glo - ry, glo-ry to God, glo-ry to God in the high - est;

F   Gm¹¹   Fmaj⁷   Gm¹¹   F   Gm¹¹   Fmaj⁷   Gm¹¹

*rit.*

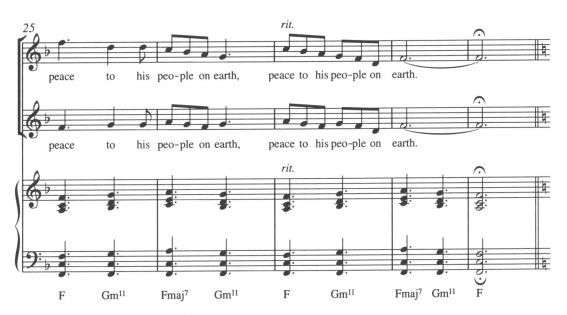

peace to his peo-ple on earth, peace to his peo-ple on earth.

peace to his peo-ple on earth, peace to his peo-ple on earth.

*rit.*

F   Gm¹¹   Fmaj⁷   Gm¹¹   F   Gm¹¹   Fmaj⁷   Gm¹¹   F

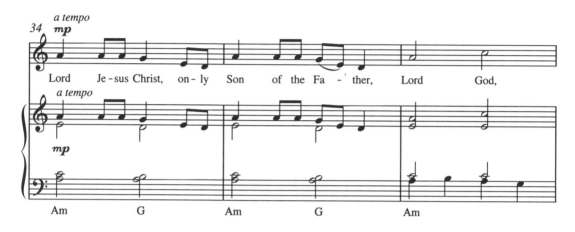

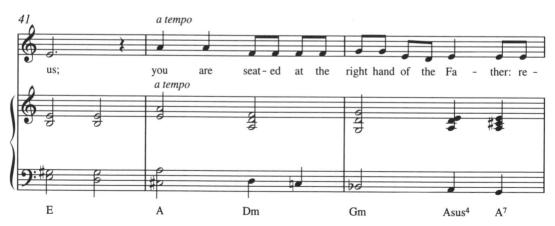

*un poco rall.*

ceive our prayer, re - ceive our prayer, re - ceive our prayer.

Dm    Esus⁴   E   Am    Dm    Esus⁴   E   Am

**Tempo I**    *un poco rall.*

*mf*

F    Gm¹¹    Fmaj⁷    Gm¹¹    Fmaj⁷    Gm¹¹    Fmaj⁷    Gm¹¹

*a tempo*

You    a-lone are the Ho - ly One,    you    a-lone are the Lord,

*a tempo*

F    Gm¹¹    Fmaj⁷    Gm¹¹    F    Gm¹¹    Fmaj⁷    Gm¹¹

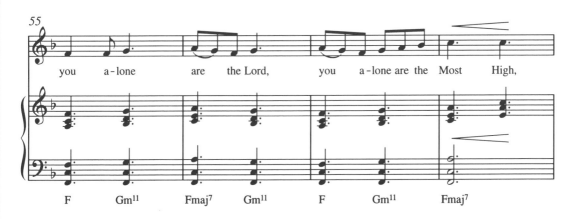

you    a-lone    are the Lord,    you    a-lone are the Most    High,

F    Gm¹¹    Fmaj⁷    Gm¹¹    F    Gm¹¹    Fmaj⁷

# SANCTUS

san - na, ho - san - na, ho - san - na in the high - est, ho -

san - na, ho - san - na, ho - san - na in the high - est, ho -

F    Dm    Gm    F    Gm    C

san - na, ho - san - na, ho - san - na in the high - est.

san - na, ho - san - na, ho - san - na in the high - est.

F    Dm    F    Bbmaj⁷    C⁷sus⁴    C⁷    F

# AGNUS DEI

take a - way the sins of the world: have mer - cy on us.

F     Gm     Am     Dm     Gm⁷     Csus⁴     C

**Optional descant**

Je - sus, Lamb of God, Je - sus, Lamb of God, you take a - way the

Je - sus, Lamb of God, Je - sus, Lamb of God, you take a - way the

F     Gm¹¹     Fmaj⁷     Gm¹¹     F     Dm⁷     Gm     C     F     Fmaj⁷     Gm

sins of the world: grant us your peace, grant us your peace.

sins of the world: grant us your peace, grant us your peace.

Am     Dm     Gm⁷     F     B♭maj⁷     C⁷sus⁴     C⁷     F

# MASS OF THE BREAD OF LIFE

Margaret Rizza

Flute or Violin
(Oboe, Recorder)

### KYRIE

### GLORIA

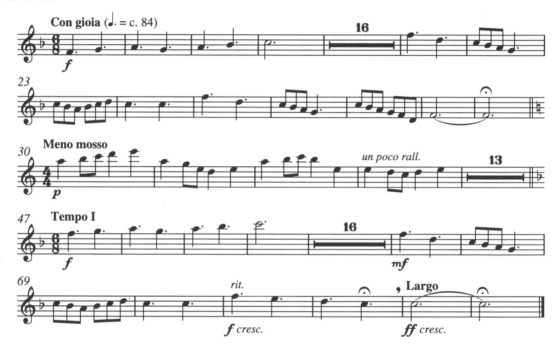

### SANCTUS

# AGNUS DEI

# MASS OF THE BREAD OF LIFE

Margaret Rizza

**Bass**
**'Cello or Bassoon**

**KYRIE**

**GLORIA**

# SANCTUS

# AGNUS DEI

*Please photocopy this page*

# KEVIN MAYHEW EASY COPYRIGHT CLEARANCE

The music in this book is protected by copyright and must not be reproduced in any way without the proper permission.

A one-year licence to reproduce the congregational parts only of *Mass of the Bread of Life* for non-commercial use may be obtained from the Kevin Mayhew Copyright Department by sending a copy of this page together with your payment.

**Name of Church** _____

**Contact Name** _____

**Address** _____

_____

**Postcode** _____

**Telephone Number** _____

**Fax Number** _____

**E-mail** _____

**Fees for one-year licence**

Fee due = £9.40. This fee is valid until 31 December 1998. After that date please contact the Copyright Department for information.

Please enclose payment by cheque or fill in the details of your Visa/Mastercard number below.

| | | | | | | | | | | | | | | |
|---|---|---|---|---|---|---|---|---|---|---|---|---|---|---|

Expiry date until end _____

Signed _____

- - - - - - - - - - - - - - - - - - - - - - - - - - - - - - - - - - - - - - - - - - - - - - - - - - - - - - - - - -

**To be completed by Kevin Mayhew Ltd**

Payment of £9.40 received. Thank you.

**Permission is granted** subject to the following further conditions:

1. that the composer is acknowledged on every copy.

2. that the following copyright line is included on every copy:

> Copyright Kevin Mayhew Ltd.
> Reproduced by permission from *Mass of the Bread of Life*.

> Licence Number _____ This Licence expires on _____

Signed for Kevin Mayhew Ltd _____

Copyright Department, Kevin Mayhew Ltd, Rattlesden, Bury St Edmunds, Suffolk IP30 0SZ
Telephone number: UK 01449 737978       International +44 1449 737978
Fax number: UK 01449 737834       International +44 1449 737834
E-mail: copyright@kevinmayhewltd.com

# MASS OF THE BREAD OF LIFE

Congregation

Margaret Rizza

## KYRIE

## GLORIA

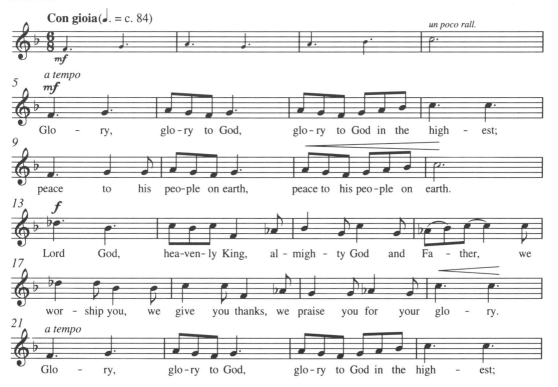

# SANCTUS

# AGNUS DEI

Je - sus, Lamb of God, Je - sus, Lamb of God, you

take a - way the sins of the world: have mer - cy on us.

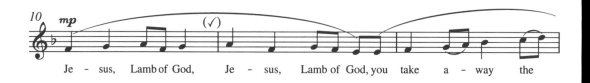

Je - sus, Lamb of God, Je - sus, Lamb of God, you take a - way the

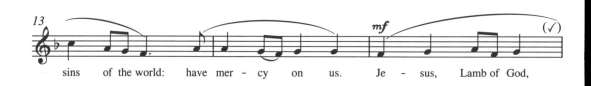

sins of the world: have mer - cy on us. Je - sus, Lamb of God,

Je - sus, Lamb of God, you take a - way the sins of the world;

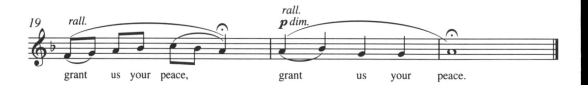

grant us your peace, grant us your peace.